DONATO'S
POLITICAL CARTOONS

THE SUN

KEY PORTER BOOKS

Canadian Cataloguing in Publication Data

Donato, Andy, 1937–
    From there to here

A Collection of cartoons which appeared in The Toronto sun
ISBN 0-919493-23-8
1. World politics – 1975-1985 – Caricatures and cartoons.
2. Canadian wit and humor, Pictorial.
3. Canada – Politics and government – 1980-   – Caricatures and
cartoons.* I. The Toronto sun.   II. Title

NC1449.D66A4 1983   741.5'971   C83-099067-4

Key Porter Books
59 Front Street East
Toronto, Ontario M5E 1B3

The Toronto Sun
333 King Street East
Toronto, Ontario M5A 3X5

Printed and bound in Canada.

Foreword

In some ways I may be the wrong person to give an objective, dispassionate assessment of Andy Donato's cartooning, since for going on 12 years as catcher on the *Toronto Sun*'s softball team he has never managed to get a throw to me at second base on target. Every time I drop the ball it is his fault.

In other ways I am the perfect person to introduce him — assuming he still needs introducing to people who buy books like this, or even those who get them as presents from others. For 11 years as editor-in-chief of the *Sun*, before I turned over the job to someone better-looking than myself, I was Donato's boss. Prior to that I was his colleague at the *Toronto Telegram*, which went out of business, no fault to Donato. During both periods he has been a good friend, albeit a trifle unpredictable and with a sense of humor you have to be careful or else he'll set you up and embarrass you horribly.

I know all the foibles of Donato. I know the real Donato — and forget all that bumph about him being born in 1937 in Scarborough, Ont., a graduate of Danforth Technical School in 1955 and going to work for T. Eaton Co. as a layout artist. That is smokescreen to make him seem seem normal.

So what if he was fired from Eaton's in 1959 because they wouldn't give him a raise? So what that he joined the promotion department of the *Tely* as an all-purpose artist, eventually becoming the paper's art director in 1968 and filling in with editorial cartoons? That's smokescreen to make people think he's an ordinary, ambitious Italian boy who likes girls, the Blue Jays, and can sound more like Fr. Guido Sarducci on *Saturday Night Live* than Fr. Guido Sarducci sounds.

Donato is like no other editorial cartoonist in captivity. And I should know because I've had to nurse him through 11 tumultuous years at the Sun where he became, by every measurable criterion, the best, funniest, most biting cartoonist in Canada. On second thought, not just Canada, but the world.

Donato fools a lot of people that he's easy-going, untemperamental, incredibly fast and multi-talented. That's an act. And just because he's had some 15 major art shows in the past 15 years, in such diverse places as London, Johannesburg, New York, Toronto and Beamsville (Beamsville? — well, no, not Beamsville, that's a joke; make it Hamilton), is no reason to think you can afford an original. You can't. The price keeps going up. Donato makes prints for poorer people, and still gets too much money for them.

Just because he excels at everything he attempts (with the possible exception of baseball), is no reason to resent him. All things considered, it is in editorial cartooning that he stands alone and unique — ask any politician. He has won the National Newspaper Award for cartooning, and to the eternal shame of that body he hasn't won it every year he enters. The judges need a saliva test. But that's me talking — and the public — not Donato, who also puts on an act of being modest and a nice-guy. One year when he didn't win the Canadian best cartoon award he won the world's best cartoon award at Montreal's prestigious International Salon of Cartoons.

What was good enough for the world, missed in Canada. That tells you something about Canadian judging.

As former editor-in-chief I can tell a hitherto well-guarded secret: In all those years of acclaim, the very best cartoons Donato did were based on ideas that I gave him; the worst, or the cartoons that offended people, were ones he did without my help. I don't like to make a big deal over that, but I know Andy would want the truth to be known. After all, drawing little pictures is nothing compared to getting great ideas after they are drawn.

To get some insight into Donato here are the four questions he's most often asked, together with his answers — and my answers, which will help readers reach their own conclusions:

Question: Where do your ideas come from?

Donato: I really don't know. Sometimes it takes hours to think of something, sometimes a few seconds, a flash. I read something, then I laugh, get angry, or sad, and want to react.

Me: An almost honest answer. It's how I write editorials too. It's the ideas that come during the hot flashes that Donato mentions that we worry about. Those are usually the incredibly vulgar cartoons that he seems most proud of and wind up being complained about to press councils — and carried in wallets.

Q: How long does it take you to draw a cartoon?

A: Sometimes half an hour, sometimes 3½ hours. It depends.

Me: Yes — it depends whether he's got a ball game to go to, an assignation or Winston's restaurant with the publisher. Donato is living proof of Parkinson's law — he can do anything in the time available for him to do it.

Q: What does the little bird in the cartoon mean?

A: Nothing. A trademark. I once had a budgie named Aaron and drew him in a few cartoons, and when I left him out people called to find out where he was. Birds are smart — they fly south in winter.

Me: The bird's a fraud. Sometimes I have even drawn it in to help Andy, and not one person ever phoned to say how much better or worse the bird looked. There are some who think Donato's cartoons are merely a vehicle for that damned, pushy, ugly little bird.

Q: Do people get angry when you draw them in a cartoon?

A: No, hardly ever. They usually want the original, though Prime Minister Trudeau once called me a son of a bitch.

Me: The PM has called everyone that, so it doesn't mean much. Some people are relieved when Donato doesn't draw them — like Publisher Creighton's martini glass, Prime Minister Begin whom he draws to resemble Fagan, Idi Amin whose cartoons make human rights zealots angry, and the Queen whom he makes look like Philip in drag.

This, then, is a glimpse at Andy Donato. If you want to know more about him, read further and study the cartoons of the most versatile and imaginative artist in newspaper work. And if you have great ideas of your own, phone him. He loves to hear from folks.

Too bad he's such a so-so baseball player.

Peter Worthington
Toronto
September, 1983

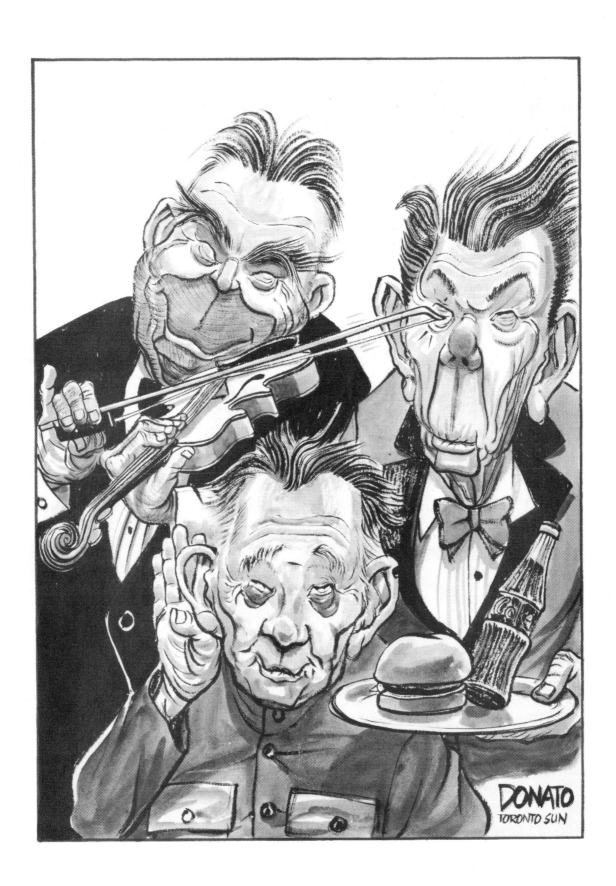

DONATO
TORONTO SUN

I'M SORRY BUT THE PRIME MINISTER IS ENGAGED WITH PREPARATIONS IN THE EVENT BRITAIN GOES TO WAR
DONATO
TORONTO SUN

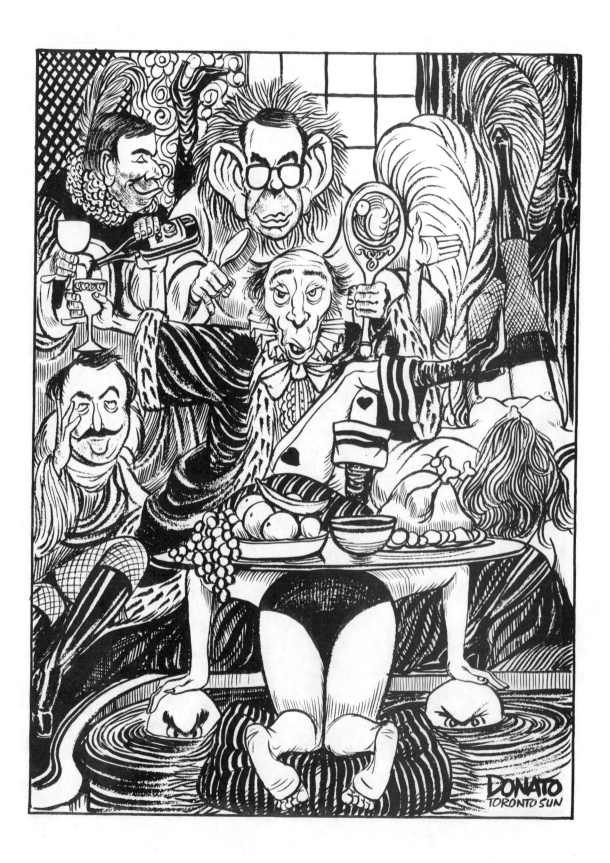

NATIONAL
ENERGY POL

DONATO
TORONTO SUN

TOMORROW ... TOMORROW

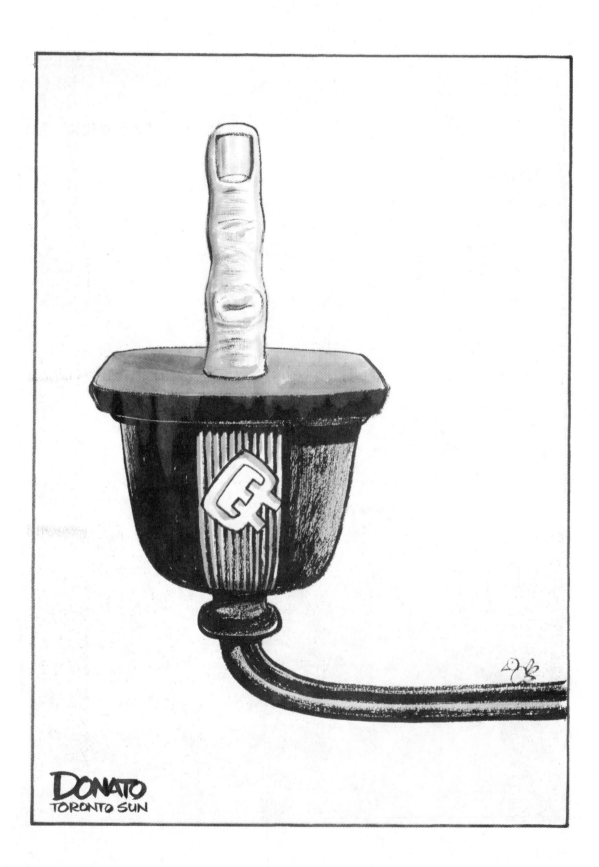

DONATO
TORONTO SUN

"STEADY AS SHE GOES"

DONATO
TORONTO SUN

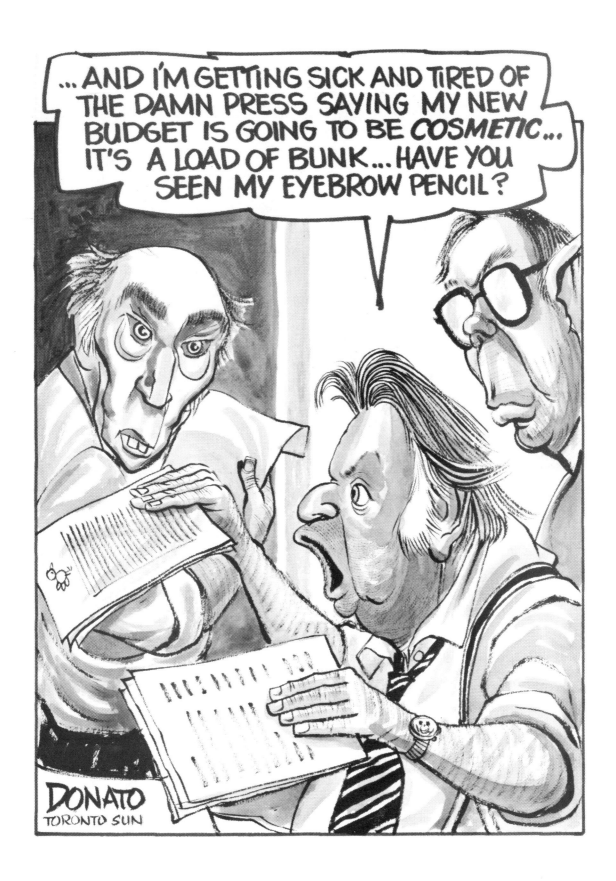

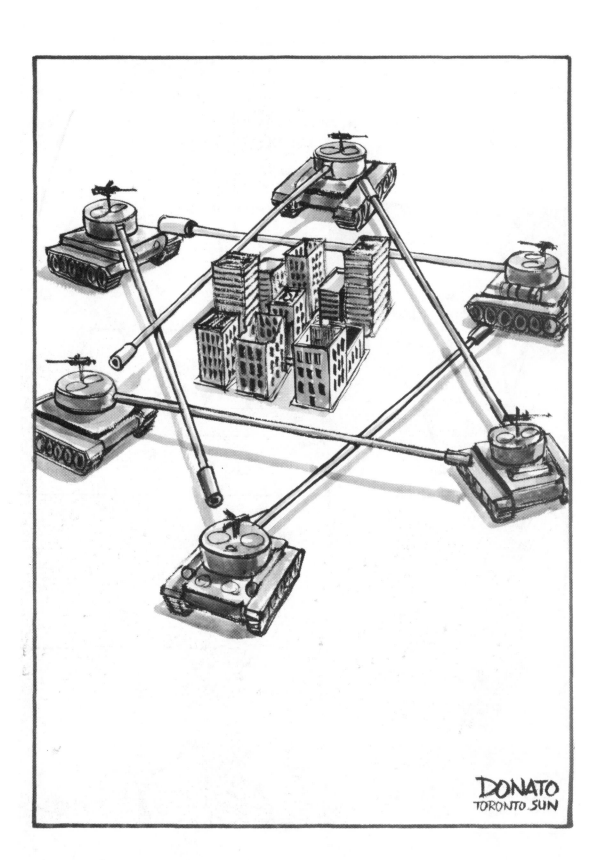

DONATO
TORONTO SUN

DONATO
TORONTO SUN

BUDGET

CANADA
CANADA
CANADA
CANADA
CANADA
CANADA

FRANKLY, I FELT SAFER BEFORE!
GUARDIAN Angel
IAN
el
DONATO TORONTO SUN

DONATO *TORONTO SUN*

EATON'S SANTA CLAUS PARADE

DONATO
TORONTO SUN

DONATO
TORONTO SUN

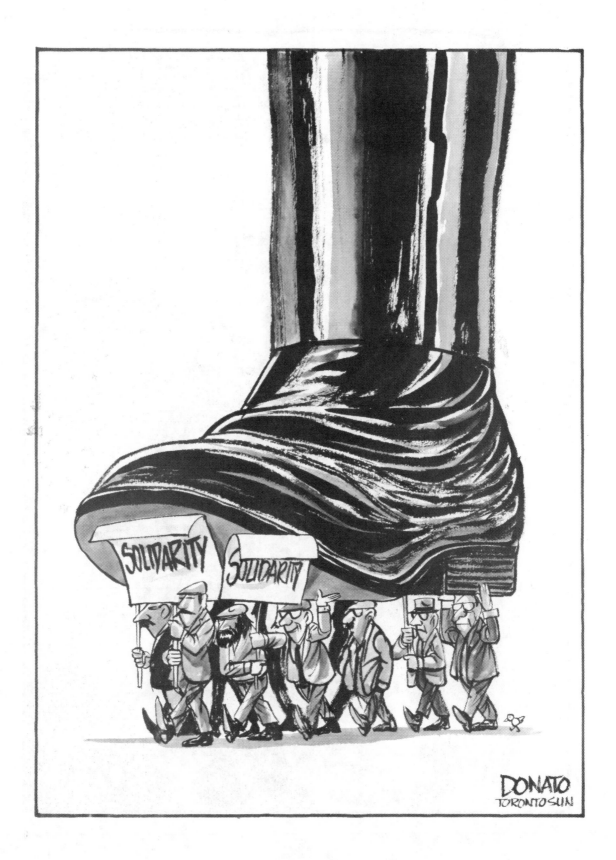

CANADA

&

WORKING
TOGETHER

DONATO TORONTO SUN

DONATO
TORONTO SUN

TO JOHN ROBARTS
TWO YEARS AGO IN JUNE
THIS WAS YOU.
THIS IS WHAT A FRIEND
WILL ALWAYS REMEMBER.

ANDY DONATO

NEWS ITEM: *A BLANKET IS PLACED OVER THE CAMERA DURING PRIME MINISTER TRUDEAU'S ADDRESS TO THE NATION TO MUFFLE THE SOUND.*

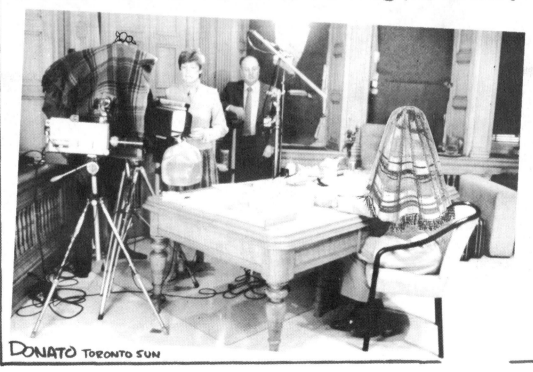

DONATO TORONTO SUN

DONATO
TORONTO SUN

TODAY'S QUIZ

THE PEOPLE IN THE ABOVE PICTURE ARE:

A. *ATTENDING A BANK ROBBERS' CONVENTION.*
B. *ATTENDING A HALLOWE'EN PARTY.*
C. *ATTENDING A LONE RANGER FAN CLUB MEETING.*
D *ATTENDING A LIBERAL PARTY FUND RAISING DINNER.*

DONATO
TORONTO SUN

DONATO
TORONTO SUN

ROBERT ELGIE
CONSUMER AFFAIRS

DONATO TORONTO SUN

HENRY MORGENTALER

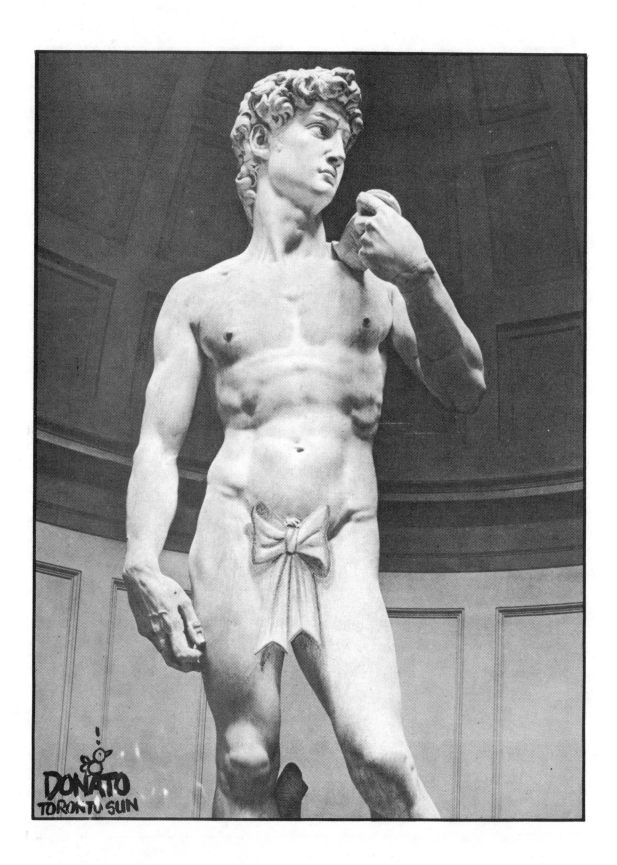

DONATO *TORONTO SUN*

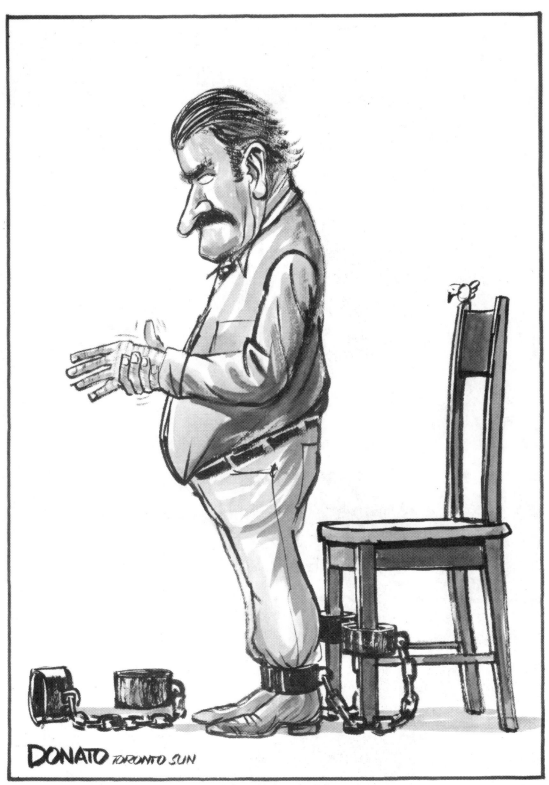

FREEDOM

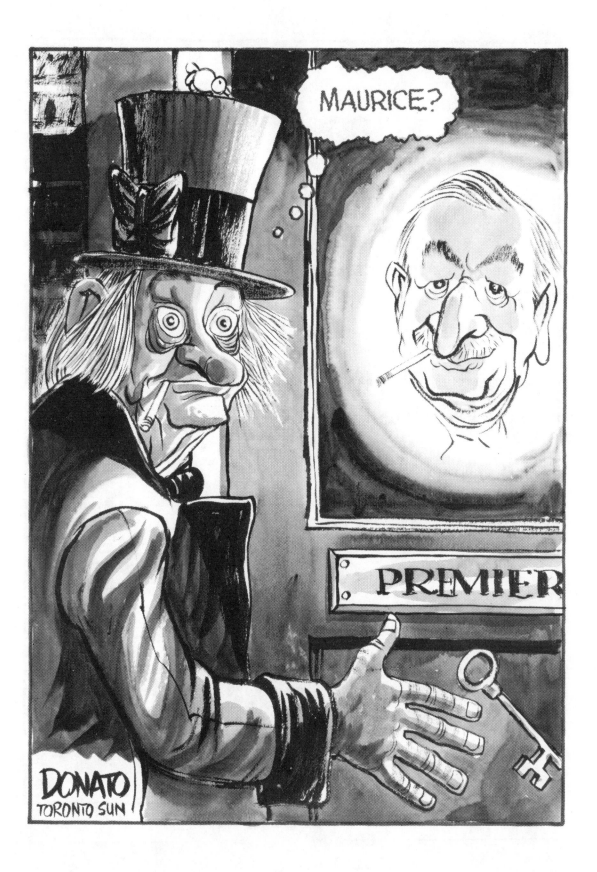

DONATO TORONTO SUN

ANOTHER PROFOUND STATEMENT BY THE PHILOSOPHER KING

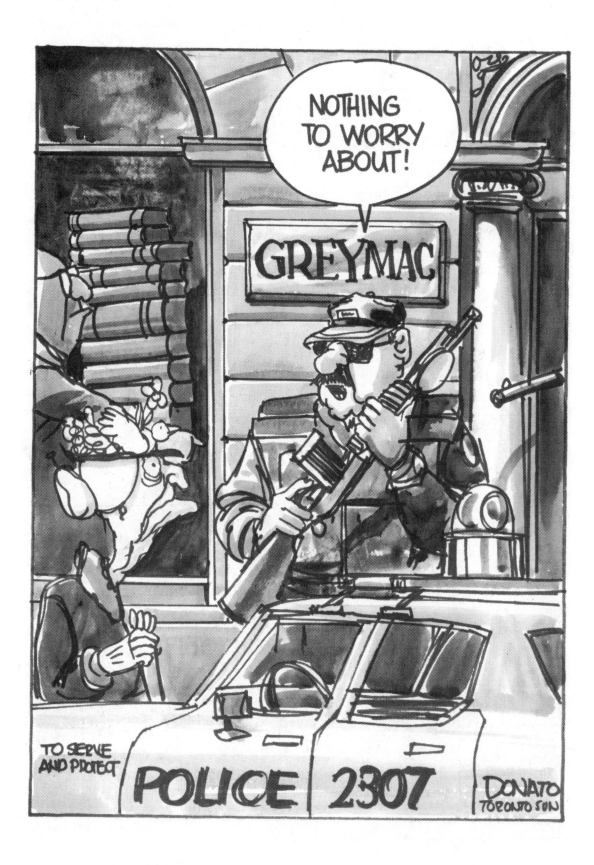

WISH YOU WERE HERE!

DONATO TORONTO SUN

THE NEWS

KIDS COST TOO MUCH
COUPLE GIVES THEM UP
TO CHILDRENS AID

JUST CAN'T GET BY
ON $768.00 PER. MO.

DONATO
TORONTO SUN

DONATO'S EASY GUIDE TO
THE GREYMAC STORY
SAUDI INVESTORS
CADILLAC FAIRVIEW
GREYMAC TRUST
GREYMAC MORTGAGE
SEAWAY MORTGAGE
SEAWAY TRUST
TOUCHE ROSS
MACDONALD CARTIER TRUST
CIBC
CROWN TRUST
KILDERKIN INVESTMENTS
435713 ONTARIO INC
MAYSFIELD PROPERTY MAN
EXTENDICARE LTD.
CLARKSON CO.
VICTORIA & GREY TRUST
CANADIAN DEPOSIT INSURANCE CO
PROVINCIAL GOV'T
FEDERAL GOV'T
O.P.P.
R.C.M.P.
OSC
MURPHY PIE COMPANY

PRAVDA

EGGLETON DECLARES TORONTO NUCLEAR FREE ZONE

DONATO
TORONTO SUN

POVERTY
LINE ▽

DONATO
TORONTO SUN

DONATO
TORONTO SUN

DONATO TORONTO SUN

DONATO
TORONTO SUN

GOVERNMENT
OF CANADA

CONFLICT OF INTEREST GUIDELINES

FOR MINISTERS
AND EX-MINISTERS

GOVERNMENT of CANADA

HERE IS YOUR VERY OWN POCKET SIZE EDITION OF THE PRIME MINISTER'S *CONFLICT OF INTEREST GUIDELINES*. IT'S EASY TO USE AND CAN BE CARRIED IN EITHER POCKET OR PURSE. JUST CUT OUT ALONG THE DOTTED LINES AND FOLD ALONG CENTRE LINES

DONATO *TORONTO SUN*

THE GILLESPIE AFFAIR

DONATO *TORONTO SUN*

I'M IN MY SWEET LITTLE NEST
WAY OUT IN THE WEST
AND I'LL WATCH THE REST
OF THE WORLD GO BUY
DONATO
TORONTO SUN

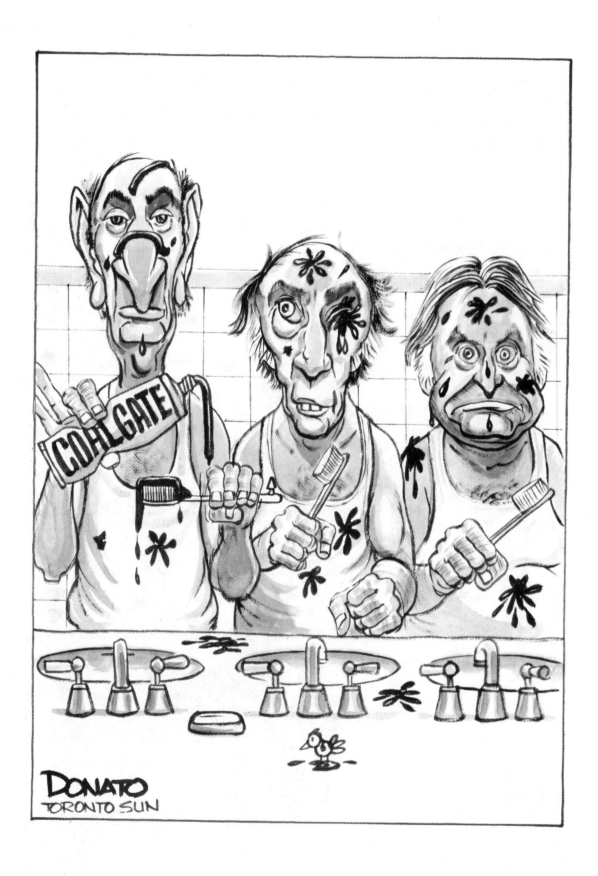

COALGATE

DONATO
TORONTO SUN

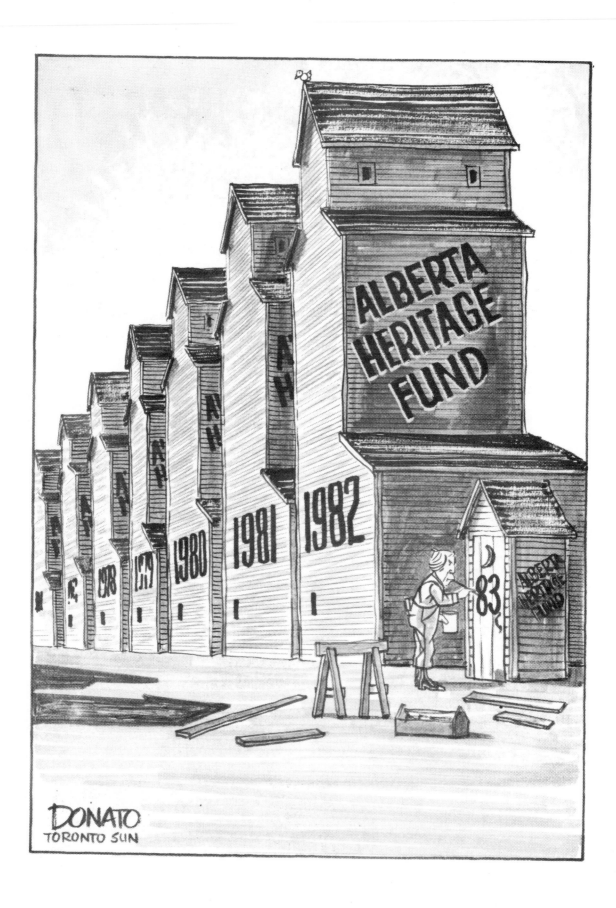

ALBERTA HERITAGE FUND

1982 1981 1980 1979 1978

83

DONATO
TORONTO SUN

SAY WHA'?

PRESS GALLERY

DONATO
TORONTO SUN

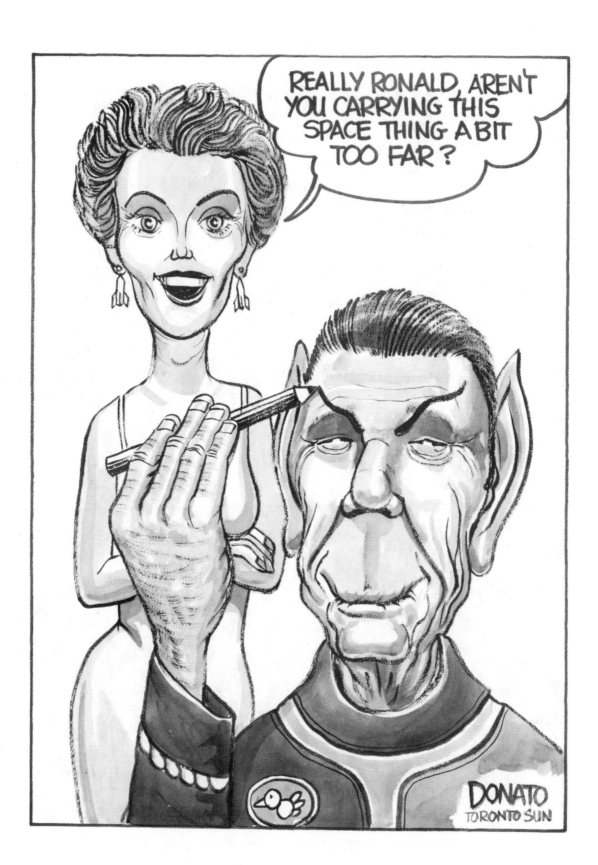

DONATO *TORONTO SUN*

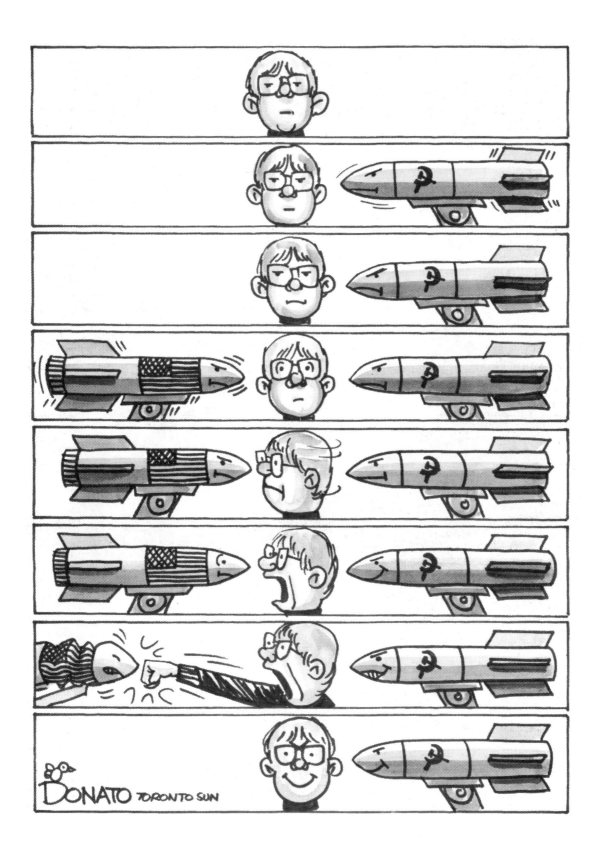

GALLUP POPULARITY CONTEST

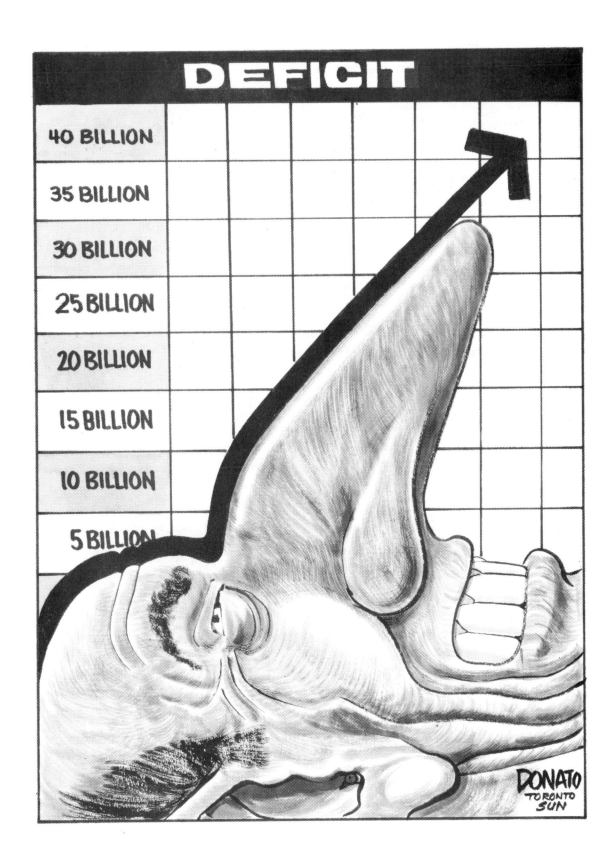

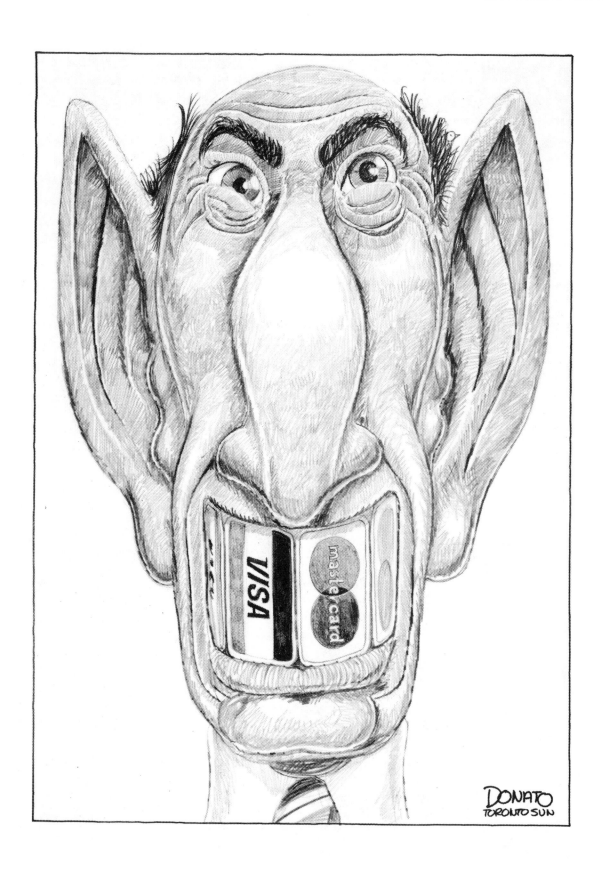

DONATO
TORONTO SUN

DONATO
TORONTO SUN

DONATO *TORONTO SUN*

DONATO
TORONTO SUN

CHANNEL

DONATO
TORONTO SUN

DONATO
TORONTO SUN

THE SUN

SUN BACKS
CROSBIE

DONATO
TORONTO SUN

DONATO
TORONTO SUN